Slip and

By Liza Charlesworth

ISBN: 978-1-339-02666-4

Art Director: Tannaz Fassihi; Designer: Tanya Chernyak
Photos © Getty Images.
Copyright © Liza Charlesworth. All rights reserved. Published by Scholastic Inc.

3 4 5 6 7 8 9 10   68   32 31 30 29 28 27 26 25 24

Printed in Jiaxing, China. First printing, August 2023.

SCHOLASTIC

See the glad kids.
Snow is a blast!

Kids can sled on a hill.
They can go fast!

Kids can hop and clap.

They can slip a lot.

Kids can sit and blab.

They can flop and flap.

See the hut with a flag.
It has snow blocks!

See the kids run and play.
Slam, blam, plop!

See the glad kid
and his snow pal.
Snow is a blast!